grade

4

For full details of exam requirements, please refer to the current syllabus in conjunction with *Examination Information & Regulations* and the guide for candidates, teachers and p[illegible] three documents are [illegible]g, as well as free of [illegible]RSM local represent[illegible]nent, The Associate[illegible]usic, 24 Portland Pla[illegible]n.

CONTENTS AND TRACK LISTING

In this album, editorial additions to the texts are given in small print, within square brackets, or – in the case of slurs and ties – in the form ⌒. Metronome marks, breath marks (retained here where they appear in the source edition) and ornament realizations (suggested for exam purposes) are for guidance only; they are not comprehensive or obligatory.

Footnotes: Anthony Burton

Alternative pieces for this grade

LIST A

- **4** **Bizet** Seguidilla (from *Carmen*). *Amazing Solos for Clarinet*, arr. Harrison (Boosey & Hawkes/MDS)
- 4 | 22 — **5** **J. F. F. Burgmüller** Ballade (Op. 100 No. 15). *Time Pieces for Clarinet*, Vol. 3, arr. Denley (ABRSM Publishing)
- 5 | 23 — **6** **Mendelssohn** Song without Words (Funeral March, Op. 62 No. 3). No. 9 from *Mendelssohn for the Clarinet*, arr. King and Frank (ABRSM Publishing)
- **7** **Mozart** Minuet (from K. 250). *Clarinet Basics Repertoire*, arr. Harris (Faber)
- 6 | 24 — **8** **Mozart** Voi che sapete (from *The Marriage of Figaro*). No. 1 from *Two Arias by Mozart*, arr. Benoy and Bryce (OUP)
- **9** **Verdi** The Force of Destiny. *Concert Repertoire for Clarinet*, arr. Harris and Johnson (Faber)

LIST B

- 10 | 28 — **4** **Badings** Siciliano (from *Reihe kleiner Klavierstücke*). *Time Pieces for Clarinet*, Vol. 3, arr. Denley (ABRSM Publishing)
- **5** **Ferguson** Prelude *or* Pastoral: No. 1 *or* No. 3 from *Four Short Pieces*, Op. 6 (Boosey & Hawkes/MDS)
- **6** **Paul Harris** Space-age Sonatina. No. 16 from *Going Solo – Clarinet*, arr. Harris and Gunning (Faber)
- 11 | 29 — **7** **Alan Haughton** Monkey Nuts: No. 17 from *Rhythm & Rag for Clarinet* (ABRSM Publishing)
- 12 | 30 — **8** **Cecilia McDowall** Romantic Song: from *Three Pastiches* (Hunt Edition/Spartan Press)
- **9** **Christopher Norton** Stick Together: No. 7 from *The Microjazz Clarinet Collection 2* (Boosey & Hawkes/MDS)

LIST C

- 16 — **4** **Richard Benger** Cantabile: from *30 Tuneful Studies for Clarinet* (Spartan Press)
- **5** **Demnitz** Study in C minor. No. 14 from *Elementarschule für Klarinette*, p. 20 (Peters)
- 17 — **6** **James Rae** Catch It!: No. 21 from *40 Modern Studies for Solo Clarinet* (Universal/MDS)
- 18 — **7** **Michael Rose** Invention: from *A Miscellany for Clarinet*, Book 2 (ABRSM Publishing)

Music origination by Barnes Music Engraving Ltd
Cover by Økvik Design
Printed in England by Halstan and Co. Ltd, Amersham, Bucks.

Allegretto

from Concert Piece No. 3 in B flat

Arranged by
Paul Harris

F. DANZI

The German composer Franz Danzi (1763–1826) was the son of an Italian-born cellist in the celebrated Mannheim orchestra. He worked as a cellist himself before becoming Kapellmeister, in charge of opera and church music, in Munich, Stuttgart – where the young Weber found him an encouraging mentor – and then Karlsruhe. Although he wrote operas, symphonies, church music and songs, he is best known today for his music for wind instruments, including some of the first wind quintets. This movement is freely adapted from the finale of the last of three Potpourris for clarinet and orchestra, published around 1818, and republished in a modern edition as a Concert Piece for clarinet and string quartet or piano.

Evening

from *Two Pieces*, Op. 26

Edited by
Colin Bradbury

O. GOLDSCHMIDT

Otto Goldschmidt (1829–1907) was a German-born pianist, composer and conductor, who became well known in late 19th-century London as vice-principal of the Royal Academy of Music, the founding conductor of the Bach Choir, and the husband of the famous soprano Jenny Lind. This is the first of his *Two Pieces* for clarinet and piano, published in 1900 with a dedication to the London clarinettist Oscar Street – although Oliver Davies, in his introduction to Colin Bradbury's edition of the work, explains that it is in fact a transcription of a German song, *Gruss an den Abend* (Greeting to the Evening), which Goldschmidt had written many years earlier.

A:3

Widmung

Op. 25 No. 1

Arranged by
Thea King and Alan Frank

SCHUMANN

Widmung Dedication

This arrangement comes from an album of songs by Robert Schumann (1810–56), freely transcribed for clarinet and piano by the clarinettist Dame Thea King and the publisher and composer Alan Frank. The original song is the first in Schumann's cycle *Myrthen*, or 'Myrtles', written in 1840 as a wedding garland for his future bride Clara Wieck. The poem is by Friedrich Rückert; the opening lines are addressed to 'You my soul, you my heart', and the middle section, at b. 14, begins 'You are rest, you are peace'.

Peacherine Rag

B:1

Arranged by
Oliver Ledbury

JOPLIN

Ragtime was a form of American popular music that had its heyday in the period around 1900; its defining characteristic was 'ragged' or syncopated rhythms against a steady beat. One of its most successful exponents was Scott Joplin (1867/68–1917), the son of a former slave, who composed a ragtime opera and many rags and other pieces for piano. This is a free adaptation of the first two strains of Joplin's *Peacherine Rag*, published in St Louis, Missouri in 1901. (Several of his pieces are named after fruits or flowers, and a peacherine is a cross between a peach and a nectarine.) The suggested metronome marking reflects the original tempo direction 'Not too fast', and Joplin's frequently repeated injunction: 'It is never right to play "rag-time" fast.' For the exam, play the dal segno but none of the other repeats.

Ground Force

JIM PARKER

Jim Parker (b. 1934) is a highly successful composer of concert works (including a Clarinet Concerto) and music for film and television; his television scores have won four British Academy Awards. His *Ground Force* theme (originally played by a brass band) was written for a popular BBC television gardening series, which ran from 1997 to 2006; in each programme, a team of experts was brought in to redesign and transform a garden rapidly and secretly while its unsuspecting owner was away. The quick tempo reflects this urgency, though a slightly slower metronome marking would be acceptable in the exam.

mp

mf

Tempo I
f

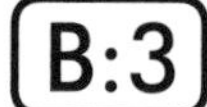

Song of the Night Sky

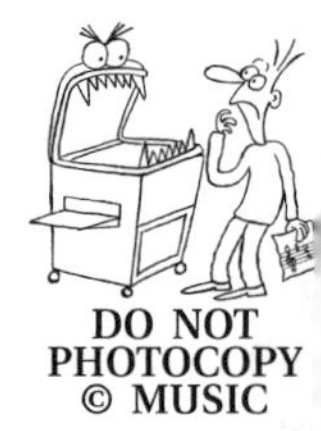

NICOLA LeFANU

Nicola LeFanu (b. 1947), daughter of the composer Elizabeth Maconchy, studied at Oxford University, the Royal College of Music and Harvard University, and since 1994 has been Professor of Music at the University of York. Her operas and concert works have been performed in many countries. *Song of the Night Sky*, LeFanu's contribution to ABRSM Publishing's album *Spectrum for Clarinet*, is dated 'York, September 2004'. She says about it: 'This nocturne is spacious and serene, but not slow: feel the tempo as a gentle one-in-a-bar, with the melody flowing onward through each phrase.'

2
mp

poco rall.
a tempo
p

poco rall.

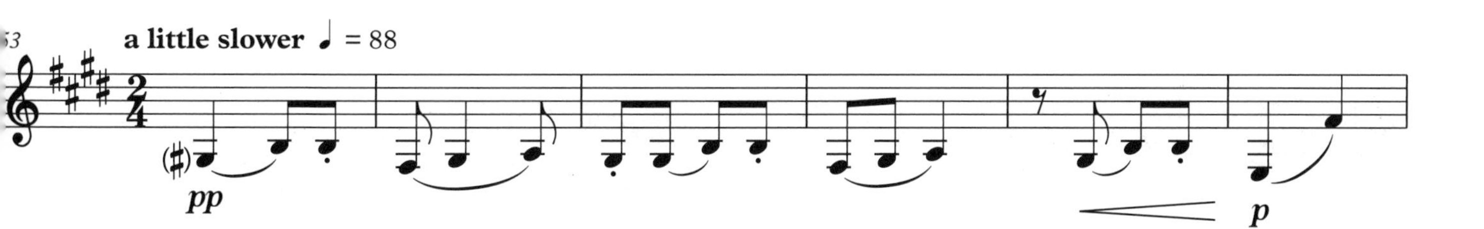
a little slower ♩ = 88
pp
p

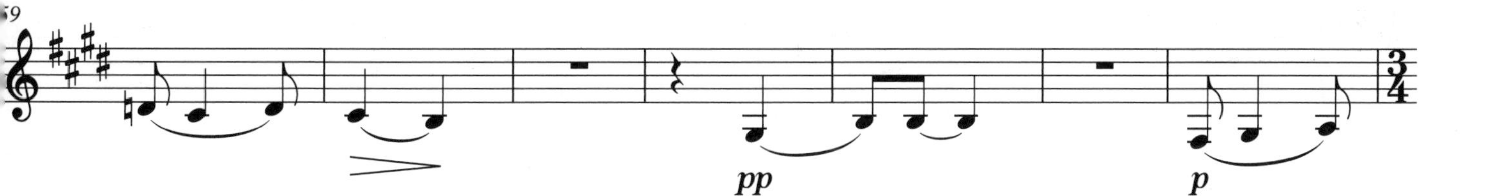
pp
p

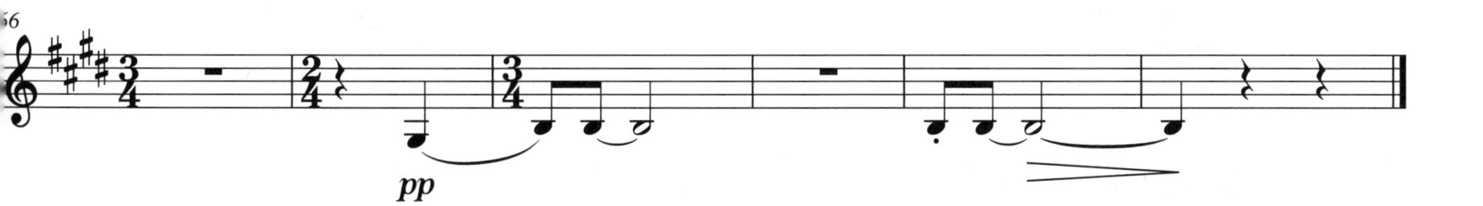
pp

Study No. 32

from *Progressive Studies for Clarinet*, Book 1

CHRIS ALLEN

Chris Allen (b. 1954) is a freelance clarinettist, teaches the instrument in Bedfordshire, and has composed a wide range of educational and concert music. This study from his *Progressive Studies*, published in two volumes by ABRSM Publishing, requires smooth playing in the lower and middle registers and careful gradation of dynamics.

Zigzag Rag

from *Cool School: Solos for Clarinet*

CHRIS GUMBLEY

Chris Gumbley (b. 1958) plays the saxophone in several jazz groups, teaches the instrument at the Birmingham Conservatoire, and has written a good deal of educational music including four *Cool School* albums of jazzy studies for clarinet, flute, and alto and tenor saxophones. In *Zigzag Rag* you will need to imagine a strict beat against which to play the syncopated ragtime rhythms.

C:3

Study in C ('The Turn')

from *New and Modern Method for the Albert and Boehm System Clarinet*

Edited by
John Davies and Paul Harris

LAZARUS

Henry Lazarus (1815–95) was one of the leading clarinettists in late 19th-century London, taught at the Royal Academy of Music and the Royal College of Music, and in 1881 published a *New and Modern Method for the Albert and Boehm System Clarinet*, incorporating material from earlier continental tutors by Berr, Müller and Neerman. This study – which in Lazarus's tutor is a duet with a simple second clarinet part – is designed to encourage fluent playing of turns; a suggested rhythmic interpretation of the notated ornament has been added.

de

Clarinet
exam pieces
Piano accompaniment

For full details of exam requirements, please refer to the current syllabus in conjunction with *Examination Information & Regulations* and the guide for candidates, teachers and parents, *These Music Exams*. These three documents are available online at www.abrsm.org, as well as free of charge from music retailers, from ABRSM local representatives or from the Services Department, The Associated Board of the Royal Schools of Music, 24 Portland Place, London W1B 1LU, United Kingdom.

REQUIREMENTS

SCALES AND ARPEGGIOS (from memory, to be played both slurred and tongued)

in F, G, A, B♭, D majors; E, G, B, C, D minors (two octaves)

Scales
in the above keys (minors in melodic *or* harmonic form at candidate's choice)

Chromatic Scale
starting on F and C (two octaves)

Arpeggios
the common chords of the above keys for the range indicated

Dominant Seventh
in the key of C (two octaves)

PLAYING AT SIGHT (see current syllabus)

AURAL TESTS (see current syllabus)

THREE PIECES — *page*

Candidates must prepare three pieces, one from each of the three Lists, A, B and C. Candidates may choose from the pieces printed in this album or any other piece listed for the grade. A full list is given in the current syllabus.

Footnotes: Anthony Burton

Music origination by Barnes Music Engraving Ltd

Cover by Økvik Design

Printed in England by Halstan & Co. Ltd, Amersham, Bucks.

In this album, editorial additions to the texts are given in small print, within square brackets, or – in the case of slurs and ties – in the form ⌒. Metronome marks, breath marks (retained here where they appear in the source edition) and ornament realizations (suggested for exam purposes) are for guidance only; they are not comprehensive or obligatory.

Allegretto

from Concert Piece No. 3 in B flat

Arranged by
Paul Harris

F. DANZI

The German composer Franz Danzi (1763–1826) was the son of an Italian-born cellist in the celebrated Mannheim orchestra. He worked as a cellist himself before becoming Kapellmeister, in charge of opera and church music, in Munich, Stuttgart – where the young Weber found him an encouraging mentor – and then Karlsruhe. Although he wrote operas, symphonies, church music and songs, he is best known today for his music for wind instruments, including some of the first wind quintets. This movement is freely adapted from the finale of the last of three Potpourris for clarinet and orchestra, published around 1818, and republished in a modern edition as a Concert Piece for clarinet and string quartet or piano.

Evening

A:2

from *Two Pieces*, Op. 26

Edited by
Colin Bradbury

O. GOLDSCHMIDT

Otto Goldschmidt (1829–1907) was a German-born pianist, composer and conductor, who became well known in late 19th-century London as vice-principal of the Royal Academy of Music, the founding conductor of the Bach Choir, and the husband of the famous soprano Jenny Lind. This is the first of his *Two Pieces* for clarinet and piano, published in 1900 with a dedication to the London clarinettist Oscar Street – although Oliver Davies, in his introduction to Colin Bradbury's edition of the work, explains that it is in fact a transcription of a German song, *Gruss an den Abend* (Greeting to the Evening), which Goldschmidt had written many years earlier.

11
p

15

18
mf
mf

21
cresc.
più cresc.
cresc.
più marcato

34

slentando

p

p

ten.

più forte

sonore

p

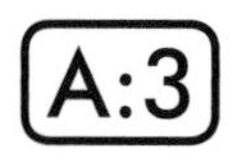

Widmung

Op. 25 No. 1

Arranged by
Thea King and Alan Frank

SCHUMANN

Widmung Dedication

This arrangement comes from an album of songs by Robert Schumann (1810–56), freely transcribed for clarinet and piano by the clarinettist Dame Thea King and the publisher and composer Alan Frank. The original song is the first in Schumann's cycle *Myrthen*, or 'Myrtles', written in 1840 as a wedding garland for his future bride Clara Wieck. The poem is by Friedrich Rückert; the opening lines are addressed to 'You my soul, you my heart', and the middle section, at b. 14, begins 'You are rest, you are peace'.

Reproduced from *Schumann for the Clarinet* arranged by Thea King and Alan Frank (ABRSM Publishing)

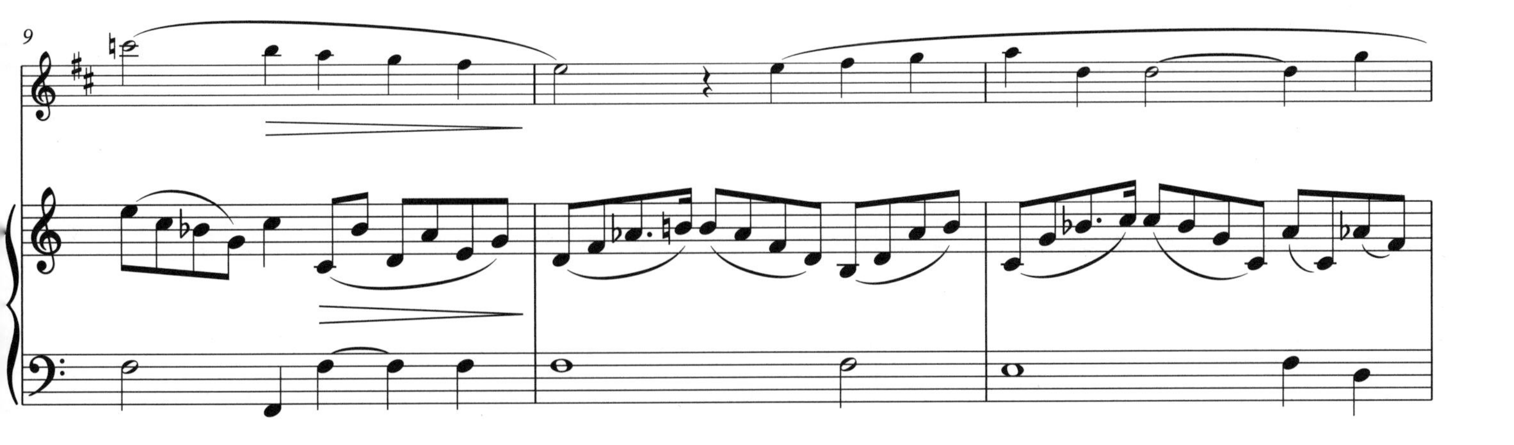
9

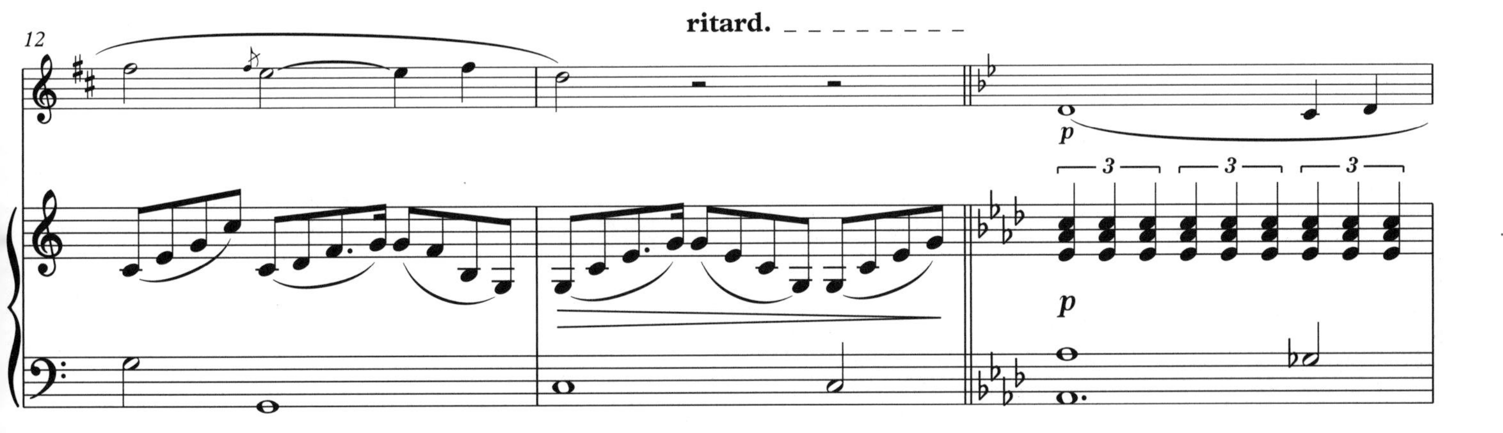
12
ritard.
p
3
3
3
p

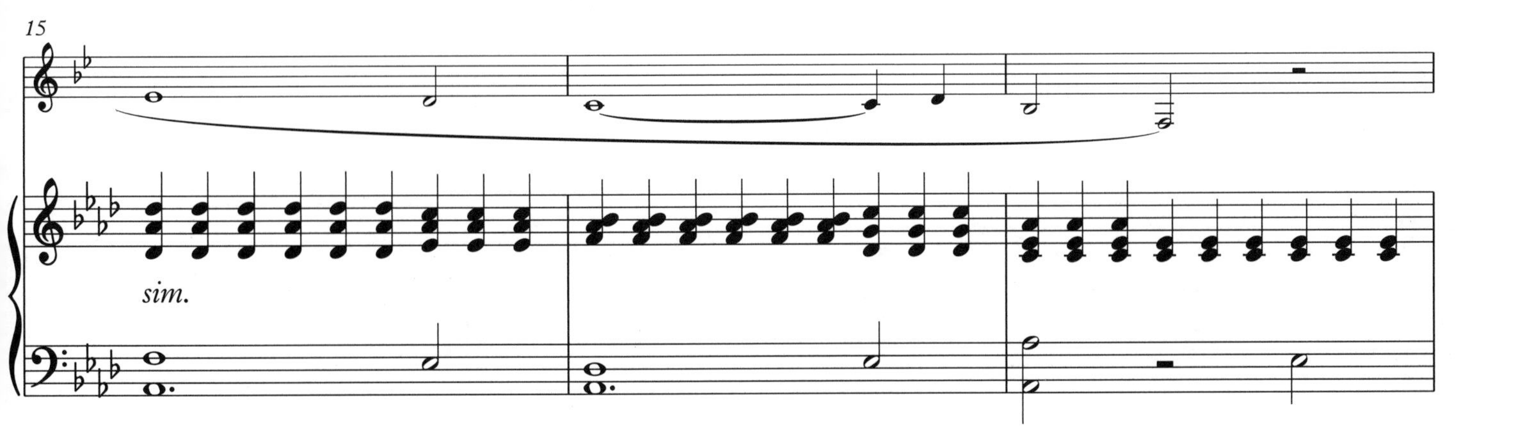
15
sim.

18

21
mp
3

24
mf
p
p

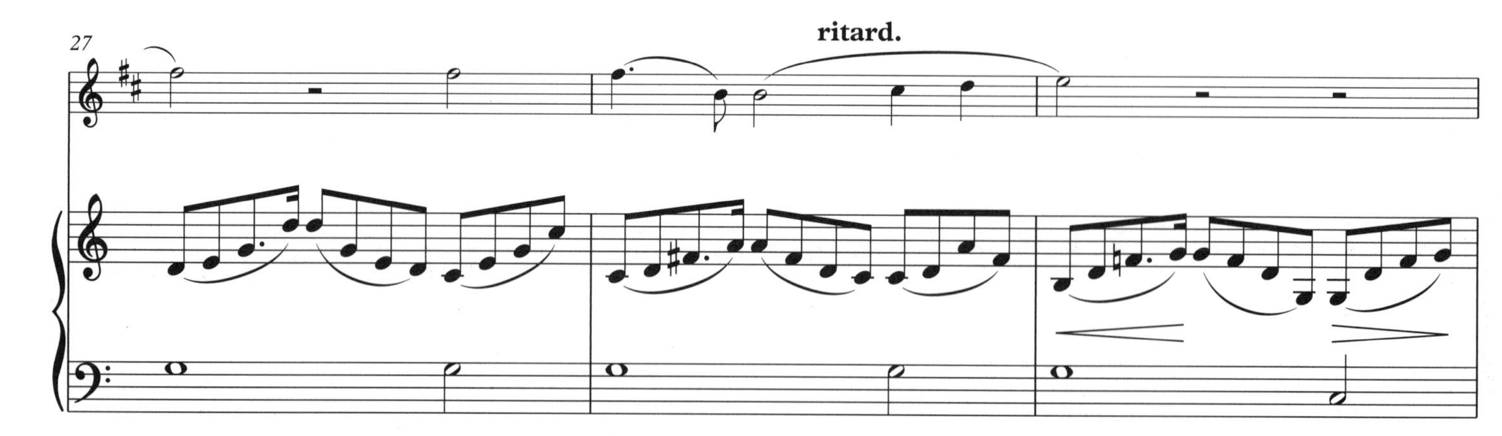
27
ritard.

a tempo
30
f
f

stringendo
33

ritard.
36

ritard.
39
mf
mf
p

ritard.
42
p

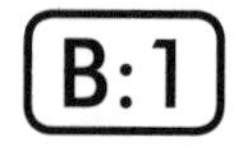

Peacherine Rag

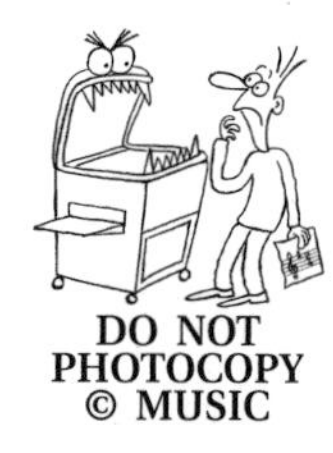

Arranged by
Oliver Ledbury

JOPLIN

Ragtime was a form of American popular music that had its heyday in the period around 1900; its defining characteristic was 'ragged' or syncopated rhythms against a steady beat. One of its most successful exponents was Scott Joplin (1867/68–1917), the son of a former slave, who composed a ragtime opera and many rags and other pieces for piano. This is a free adaptation of the first two strains of Joplin's *Peacherine Rag*, published in St Louis, Missouri in 1901. (Several of his pieces are named after fruits or flowers, and a peacherine is a cross between a peach and a nectarine.) The suggested metronome marking reflects the original tempo direction 'Not too fast', and Joplin's frequently repeated injunction: 'It is never right to play "rag-time" fast.' For the exam, play the dal segno but none of the other repeats.

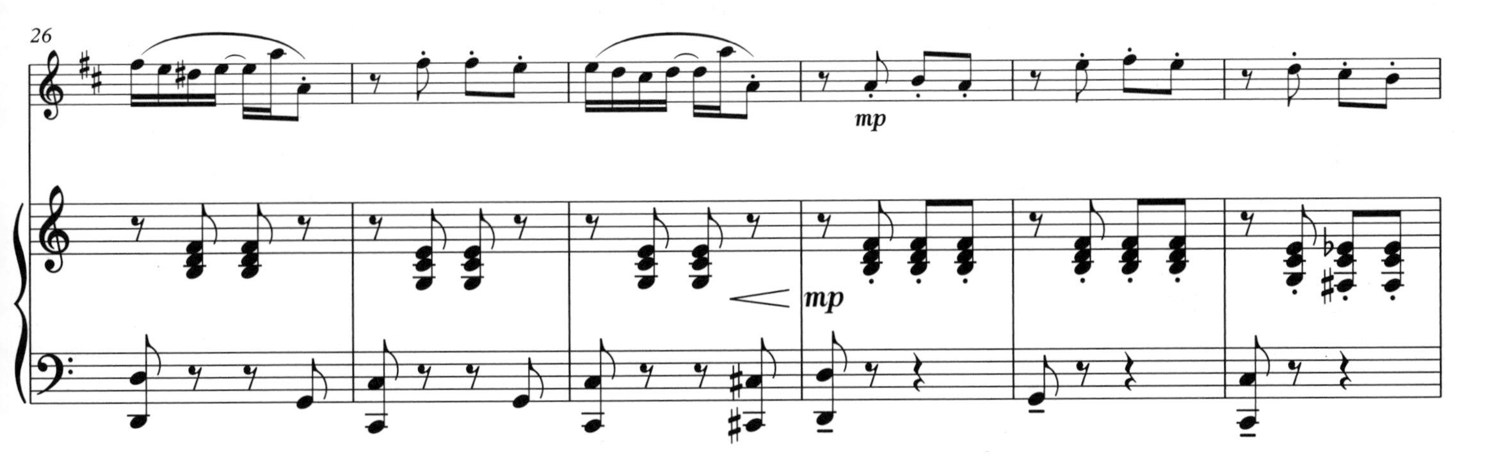

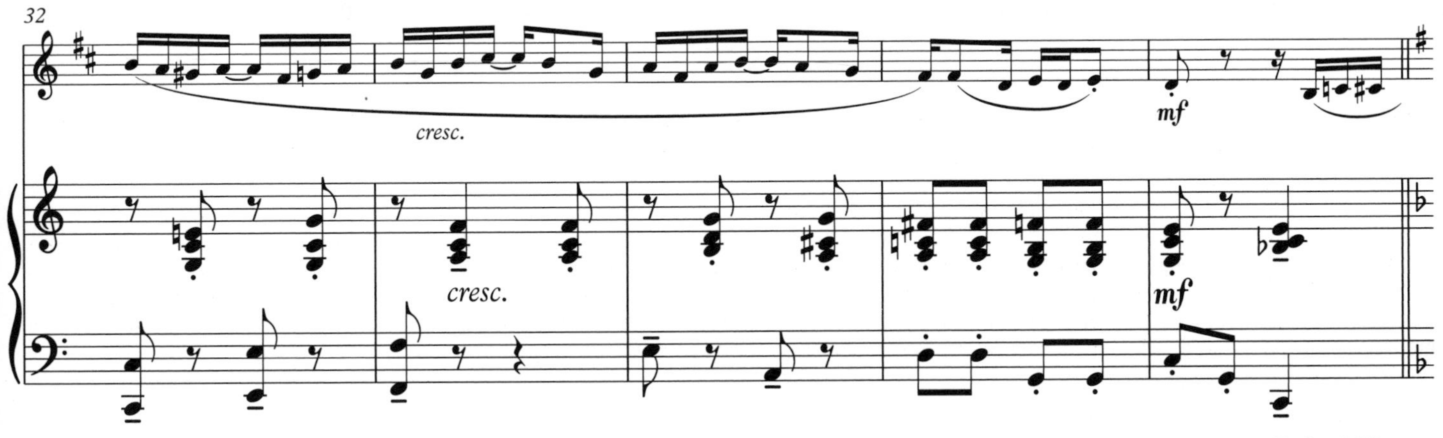

D.S. al Fine
(without repeat)

Ground Force

JIM PARKER

Jim Parker (b. 1934) is a highly successful composer of concert works (including a Clarinet Concerto) and music for film and television; his television scores have won four British Academy Awards. His *Ground Force* theme (originally played by a brass band) was written for a popular BBC television gardening series, which ran from 1997 to 2006; in each programme, a team of experts was brought in to redesign and transform a garden rapidly and secretly while its unsuspecting owner was away. The quick tempo reflects this urgency, though a slightly slower metronome marking would be acceptable in the exam.

10

13

17
meno mosso
p
p

21

25
mp

30

35
mf

39
Tempo I
f

44
f

48

51

54

B:3

Song of the Night Sky

NICOLA LeFANU

Flowing, spacious ♩ = 96–104

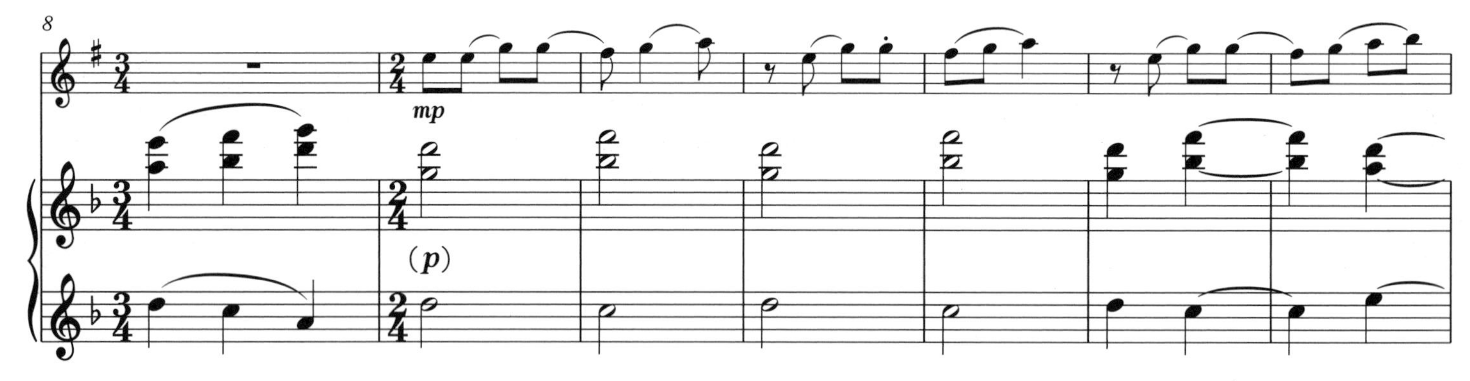

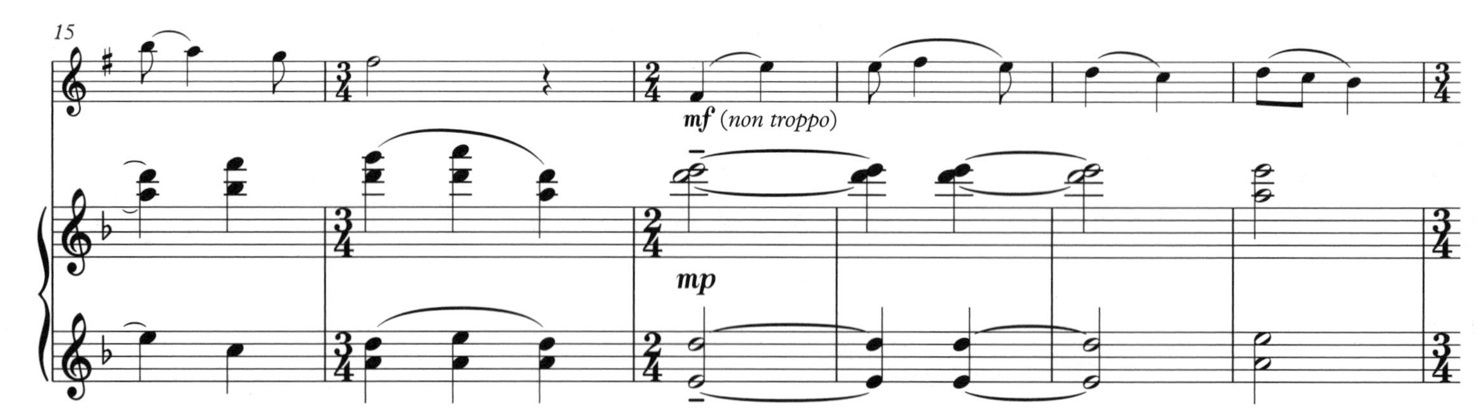

27
f
f sostenuto
f sempre

34
mp
mp

40
poco rall.
a tempo
p
p

47
poco rall.

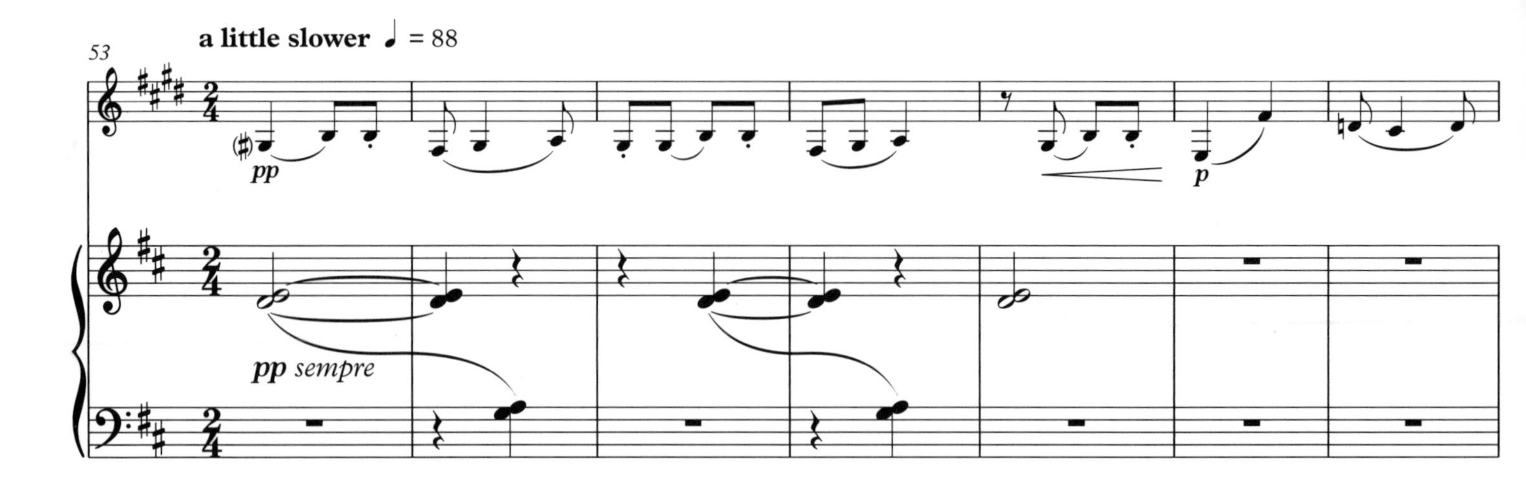

Nicola LeFanu (b. 1947), daughter of the composer Elizabeth Maconchy, studied at Oxford University, the Royal College of Music and Harvard University, and since 1994 has been Professor of Music at the University of York. Her operas and concert works have been performed in many countries. *Song of the Night Sky*, LeFanu's contribution to ABRSM Publishing's album *Spectrum for Clarinet*, is dated 'York, September 2004'. She says about it: 'This nocturne is spacious and serene, but not slow: feel the tempo as a gentle one-in-a-bar, with the melody flowing onward through each phrase.'